Garfield

on Vacation

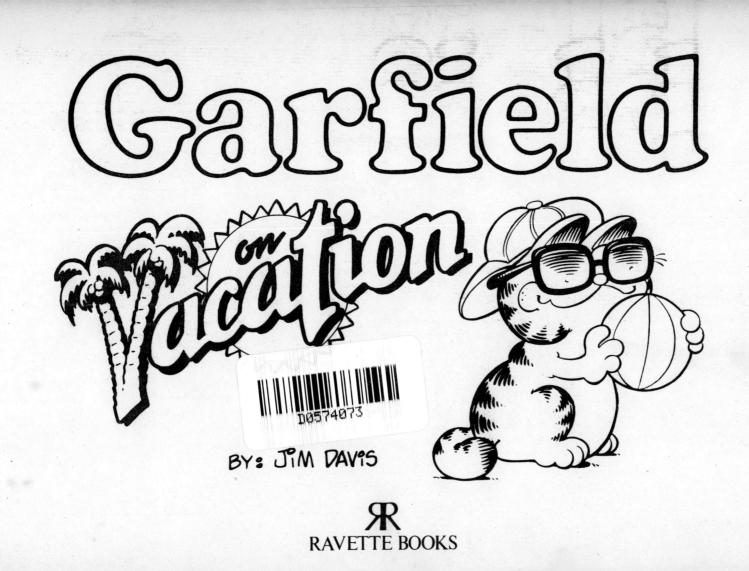

BY: JIM DAVIS

RAVETTE BOOKS

This edition first published by
Ravette Books Limited 1987

Reprinted 1988, 1989

Printed in Great Britain
for Ravette Books Limited,
3 Glenside Estate, Star Road, Partridge Green,
Horsham, West Sussex RH13 8RA
by The Guernsey Press Company Limited,
Guernsey, Channel Islands
and bound by
WBC Bookbinders Limited,
Maesteg, Mid Glamorgan.

ISBN 0 948456 15 9

on Vacation

At the suggestion of a vacation, Garfield responds to the call of the wild, the smell of fresh air and the splendour of the great outdoors. Translated, this means Garfield responds to the call of "Dinner time", the smell of fresh Lasagne and according to our homely hero, the splendid thing about the great outdoors is that it's NOT indoors!

COME ON, GARFIELD. LET'S GO CAMPING

NOT ON YOUR LIFE

© 1979 United Feature Syndicate, Inc. JIM DAVIS

GEE, AND I'D PACKED LOTS OF LASAGNA, TOO

SINCE YOU PUT IT THAT WAY, I RECKON THERE'S A TRAIL OR TWO OUT THERE THAT COULD STAND A LITTLE BLAZING

6-11

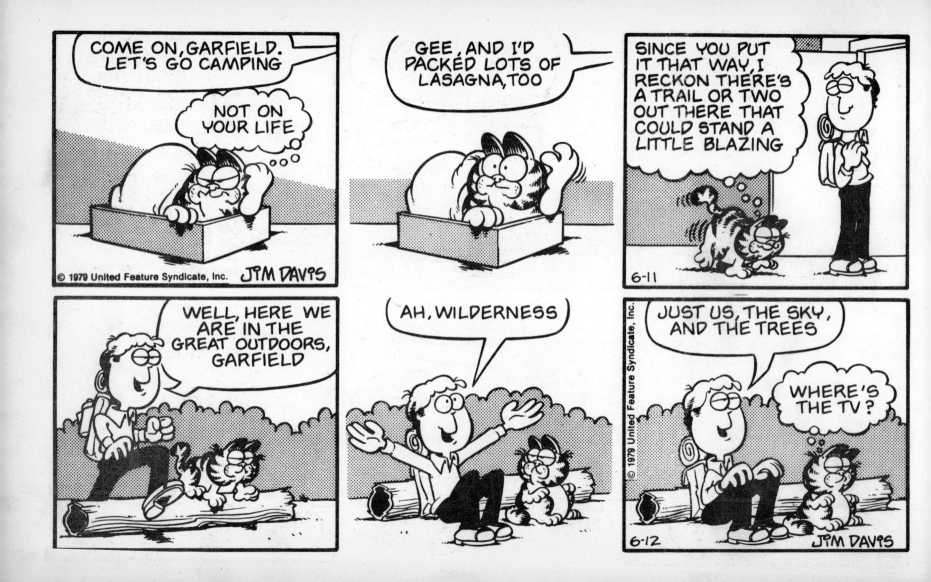

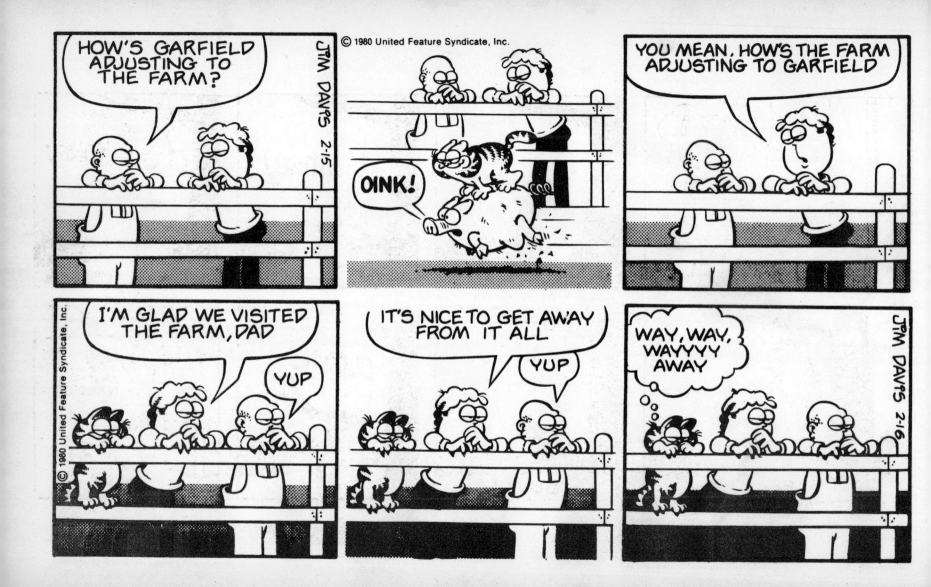

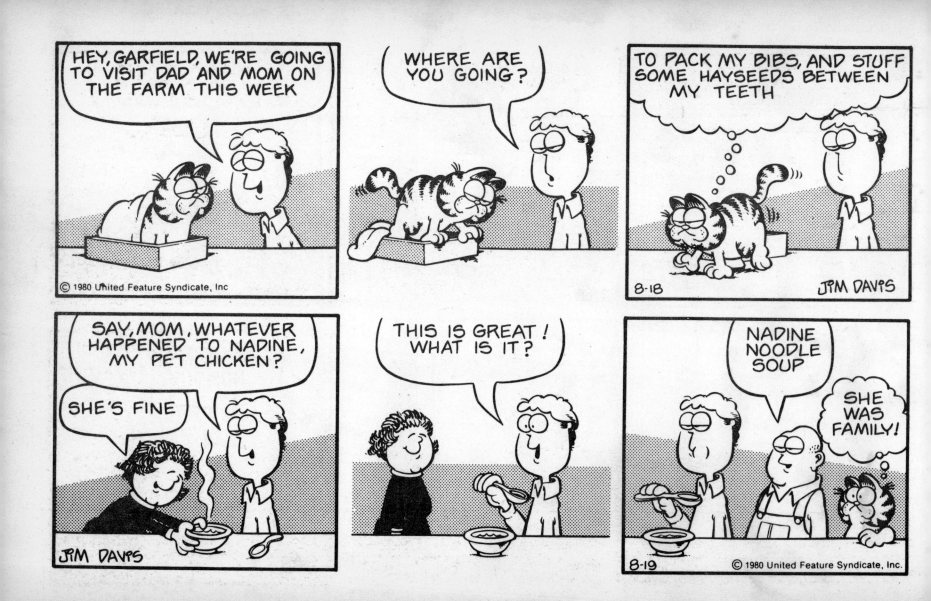

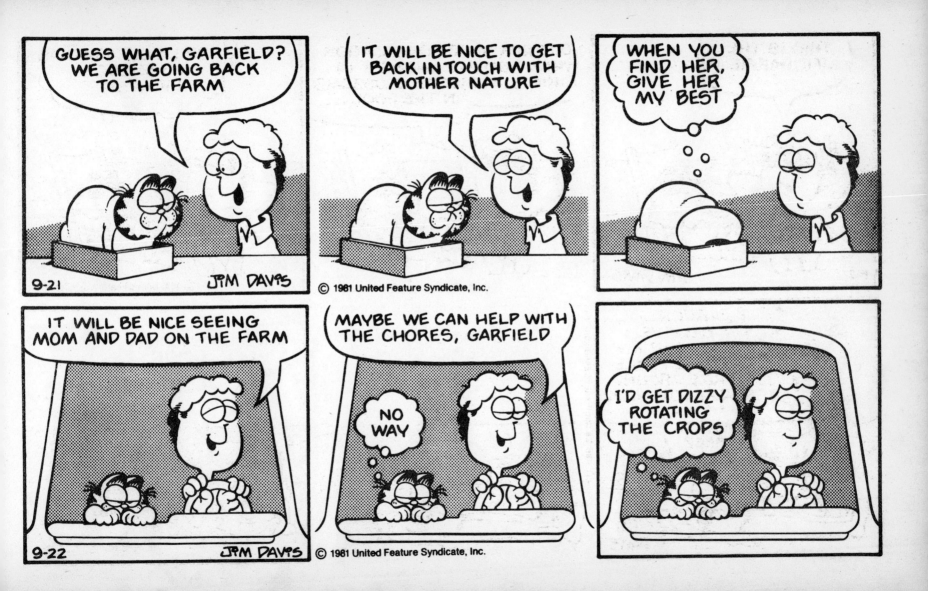

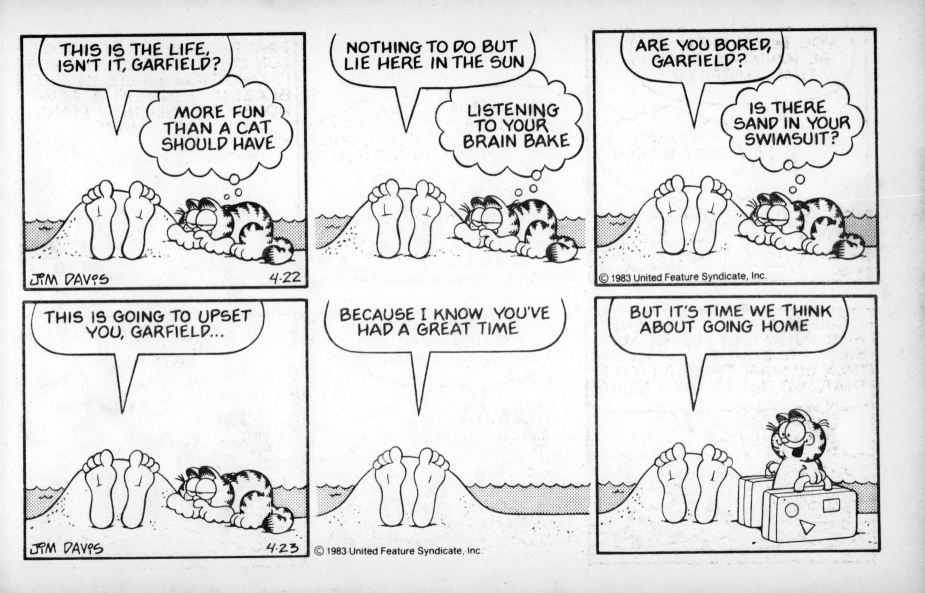

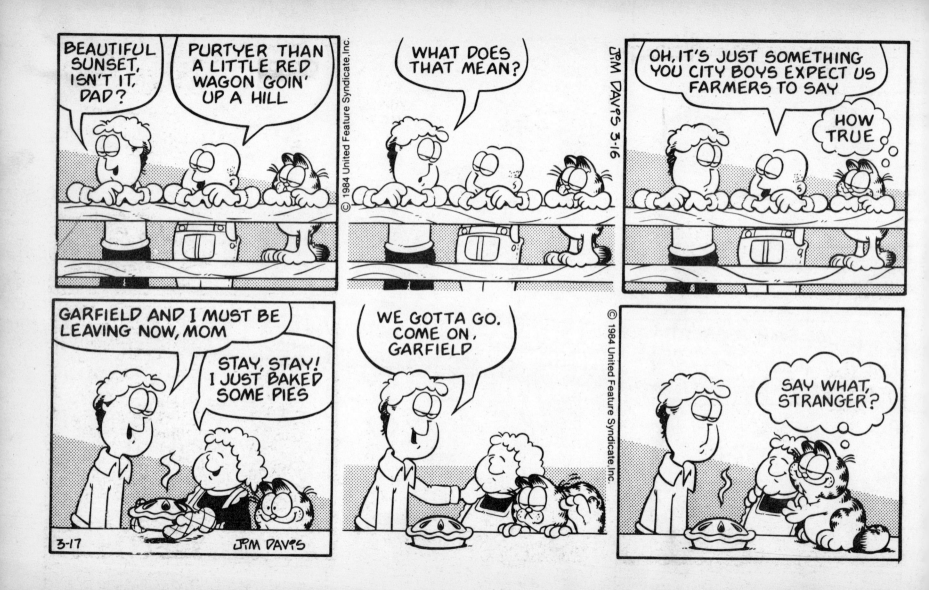

A selection of Garfield books published by Ravette

Garfield Landscapes

Garfield The All-Round Sports Star	£2.95
Garfield The Irresistible	£2.95
Garfield The Incurable Romantic	£2.95
Garfield Weighs In	£2.95
Garfield I Hate Monday	£2.95
Garfield Special Delivery	£2.95
Garfield Another Serve	£2.95
Garfield Wraps It Up	£2.95
Garfield This Is Your Life	£2.95
Garfield Sheer Genius	£2.95
Garfield Goes Wild	£2.95

Garfield Pocket-books

No. 1	Garfield The Great Lover	£1.95
No. 2	Garfield Why Do You Hate Mondays?	£1.95
No. 3	Garfield Does Pooky Need You?	£1.95
No. 4	Garfield Admit It, Odie's OK!	£1.95
No. 5	Garfield Two's Company	£1.95
No. 6	Garfield What's Cooking?	£1.95
No. 7	Garfield Who's Talking?	£1.95
No. 8	Garfield Strikes Again	£1.95
No. 9	Garfield Here's Looking At You	£1.95
No. 10	Garfield We Love You Too	£1.95
No. 11	Garfield Here We Go Again	£1.95
No. 12	Garfield Life and Lasagne	£1.95
No. 13	Garfield In The Pink	£1.95
No. 14	Garfield Just Good Friends	£1.95
No. 15	Garfield Plays It Again	£1.95
No. 16	Garfield Flying High	£1.95
No. 17	Garfield On Top Of The World	£1.95
No. 18	Garfield Happy Landings	£1.95

Garfield TV Specials

Here Comes Garfield	£2.95
Garfield On The Town	£2.95
Garfield In The Rough	£2.95
Garfield In Disguise	£2.95
Garfield In Paradise	£2.95
Garfield Goes To Hollywood	£2.95
A Garfield Christmas	£2.95

The Second Garfield Treasury	£5.95
The Third Garfield Treasury	£5.95
The Fourth Garfield Treasury	£5.95

Garfield A Weekend Away	£4.95
Garfield How to Party	£3.95

All these books are available at your local bookshop or newsagent, or can be ordered direct from the publisher. Just tick the titles you require and fill in the form below. Prices and availability subject to change without notice.

Ravette Books Limited, 3 Glenside Estate, Star Road, Partridge Green, Horsham, West Sussex RH13 8RA

Please send a cheque or postal order, and allow the following for postage and packing. UK: Pocket-books – 45p for up to two books and 15p for each additional book. Landscape Series and TV Specials – 45p for one book plus 15p for each additional book. Treasuries, How to Party and A Weekend Away – 75p for each book.

Name...

Address...

....